Ultimate
Novel
Planning
Workbook

M000236376

☑ Story title: _____

☑ Author: _____

☑ Date: _____

Copyright 2015 © Creative Cartel Publishing

All rights reserved.
No part of this publication may be reproduced or distributed in print or electronic form for commercial purposes without prior permission of the author. Please respect the hard work of the author and do not participate in or encourage the piracy of copyrighted material.

First print edition, April 2015
ISBN-10:099431390X
ISBN-13:978-0-9943139-0-4

Cover designed by: Lana Pecherczyk
Written by: Lana Pecherczyk

See Lana's Urban Fantasy books at www.ludusbooks.com
Visit Lana's writing blog at www.authorzoo.com.au
Hire Creative Cartel Publishing at www.creativecartelpublishing.com.au

Table of Contents

How to use
this workbook

Hello Writers!

This workbook has been created for anyone who
wants to tell a story ...
A long story, so long in fact that you need help planning it.
From inception, to editing and a little marketing - you will find
worksheets for it all in this book.

Start at the beginning and fill out each worksheet as you require.

Because you have purchased the print copy, you can get the printables
at 50% off at my Etsy store. Details at the end of the book.

Please respect that these worksheets are for personal use only,
do not share or redistribute for the purpose of resale.
Teachers are given special permission to use these worksheets in
a classroom environment, but do not pass the
digital file onwards.

If you are happy with the product, please take some time to help out
the author by providing an honest review online.
Thank you.

Stay strong writers.

Now, to begin your journey.

Brain Dump

Story Mind-map

If you have absolutely no where to start, use this mind-map to discover what ideas tickle your fancy. Start at the middle, work your way outwards. By the time you've filled out everything, you should have a guide as to what genre you like to write, and what plot ideas drive you.

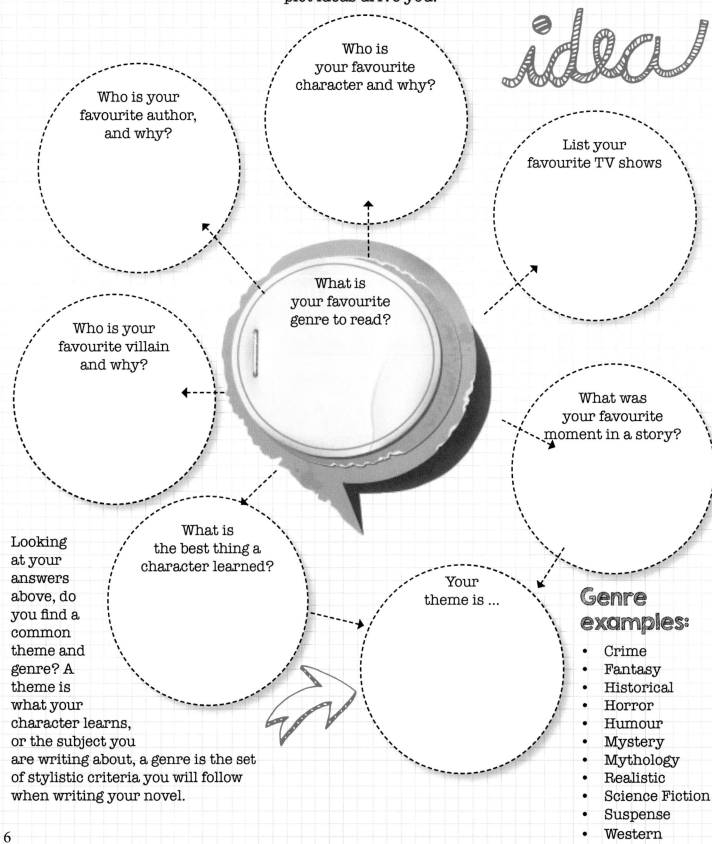

idea

Who is your favourite character and why?

Who is your favourite author, and why?

List your favourite TV shows

What is your favourite genre to read?

Who is your favourite villain and why?

What was your favourite moment in a story?

Looking at your answers above, do you find a common theme and genre? A theme is what your character learns, or the subject you are writing about, a genre is the set of stylistic criteria you will follow when writing your novel.

What is the best thing a character learned?

Your theme is ...

Genre examples:

- Crime
- Fantasy
- Historical
- Horror
- Humour
- Mystery
- Mythology
- Realistic
- Science Fiction
- Suspense
- Western

Story Brainstorm

Story Title: _____

Protagonist/Hero

BACK-STORY

Antagonist/Villain

BACK-STORY

Other characters

Hero's goal or problem to solve (internal conflict)

Obstacles in achieving goal (external conflict)

-
-
-

Setting - time & place

Genre of novel

Story theme

POV

Sub-plots (comedy, romance, suspense...)

-
-
-

Ending - resolution

Sum up your story in a few sentences

_____

_____

_____

Floor Plan

World Map

Character Name Ideas

Record the names you like for your characters. If you want to come up with something original, try thinking of the word you want to use to describe their personality, then swap some letters around, or add and remove some. For example, I want my character to be known as having courage, so ... I'm going to swap the 'C' with an 'F' and remove a couple more letters to make Furage. This would suit a high fantasy pretty well. Use your imagination, and keep in mind the genre you are writing.

Boys   Girls

Character Quirk Ideas

A 'quirk' or 'tag' is a common writing technique you use for each character to help the reader tell them apart. Use this worksheet to think of different quirks you can use for different character types. Just remember, make sure it's relevant to the plot. For example, my character is 'the frugal friend'. He wears his clothes inside out to save on laundry fees and collects spare change from meter boxes. Use a sound, visual or action.

Characteristic   Quirk/tag

Notes

Notes

Protagonist's Name:

Profile pic

Physical description:

Distinctive features:

What is their home like?:

Personality:

Occupation/education:

Religion/politics:

Background:

Likes:

Dislikes:

Family & friends:

Quirky habit/tag: *(sound, visual, action)*

Enemies:

WANTS: *(goals & motivation)*

What's stopping them from achieving goals?:

Antagonist's Name: _____

Profile pic

Physical description: _____
_____
_____
_____

Distinctive features: _____
_____
_____
_____

What is their home like?: _____

Personality: _____

Occupation/education: _____

Religion/politics: _____

Background: _____

Likes: _____

Dislikes: _____

Family & friends: _____

Quirky habit/tag: *(sound, visual, action)* _____

Enemies: _____

WANTS: *(goals & motivation)* _____

What's stopping them from achieving goals?: _____
_____
_____
_____

Character's Name: _____

Profile pic

Physical description: _____
_____
_____
_____
_____

Distinctive features: _____
_____
_____
_____
_____

What is their home like?: _____

Personality: _____

Occupation/education: _____

Religion/politics: _____

Background: _____

Likes: _____

Dislikes: _____

Family & friends: _____

Quirky habit/tag: *(sound, visual, action)*

Enemies: _____

WANTS: *(goals & motivation)*

What's stopping them from achieving goals?: _____
_____
_____
_____

Character's
Name: _____

Profile pic

Physical description: _____
_____
_____
_____
_____

Distinctive features: _____
_____
_____
_____
_____
_____

What is their home like?: _____

Personality: _____

Occupation/education: _____

Religion/politics: _____

Background: _____

Likes: _____

Dislikes: _____

Family & friends: _____

Quirky habit/tag: *(sound, visual, action)* _____

Enemies: _____

WANTS: *(goals & motivation)* _____

What's stopping them from achieving goals?: _____
_____
_____
_____

Character's Name: _____

Profile pic

Physical description:

Distinctive features:

What is their home like?:

Personality:

Occupation/education:

Religion/politics:

Background:

Likes:

Dislikes:

Family & friends:

Quirky habit/tag: *(sound, visual, action)*

Enemies:

WANTS: *(goals & motivation)*

What's stopping them from achieving goals?:

Character's Name: _____

Profile pic

Physical description: _____
_____
_____
_____

Distinctive features: _____
_____
_____
_____

What is their home like?: _____

Personality: _____

Occupation/education: _____

Religion/politics: _____

Background: _____

Likes: _____

Dislikes: _____

Family & friends: _____

Quirky habit/tag: *(sound, visual, action)*

Enemies: _____

WANTS: *(goals & motivation)*

What's stopping them from achieving goals?: _____
_____
_____

Character's Name: _____

Profile pic

Physical description:
_____
_____
_____
_____

Distinctive features:
_____
_____
_____
_____

What is their home like?:

Personality:

Occupation/education:

Religion/politics:

Background:

Likes:

Dislikes:

Family & friends:

Quirky habit/tag: *(sound, visual, action)*

Enemies:

WANTS: *(goals & motivation)*

What's stopping them from achieving goals?:

_____
_____
_____

Character's Name: _____

Profile pic

Physical description: _____
_____
_____
_____

Distinctive features: _____
_____
_____
_____

What is their home like?: _____

Personality: _____

Occupation/education: _____

Religion/politics: _____

Background: _____

Likes: _____

Dislikes: _____

Family & friends: _____

Quirky habit/tag: *(sound, visual, action)*

Enemies: _____

WANTS: *(goals & motivation)*

What's stopping them from achieving goals?: _____
_____
_____

Character List Summary

Keep track of all the characters that appear in your novel.

Name	Description	In Chapters	Pages

Character List Summary

Keep track of all the characters that appear in your novel.

Name	Description	In Chapters	Pages

Setting
Worksheet

Title:

City/Town/Region: Year/Time period:

Season:

Spring ☐   Summer ☐   Autumn ☐   Winter ☐

How does the setting and season affect the story?

Describe the setting from your major characters POV.

Protagonist: Antagonist:

○   ○

○   ○

○   ○

Touch:

Taste:

Sight:

Smell:

Sound:

Setting
Worksheet

Title:

City/Town/Region: Year/Time period:

Season:

Spring ☐   Summer ☐   Autumn ☐   Winter ☐

How does the setting and season affect the story?

Describe the setting from your major characters POV.

Protagonist: Antagonist:

○   ○

○   ○

○   ○

Touch:

Taste:

Sight:

Smell:

Sound:

Setting
Worksheet

Title:

City/Town/Region: Year/Time period:

Season:

Spring ☐   Summer ☐   Autumn ☐   Winter ☐

How does the setting and season affect the story?

Describe the setting from your major characters POV.

Protagonist: Antagonist:

○   ○

○   ○

○   ○

Touch:

Taste:

Sight:

Smell:

Sound:

Setting
Worksheet

Title:

City/Town/Region: Year/Time period:

Season:

Spring ☐   Summer ☐   Autumn ☐   Winter ☐

How does the setting and season affect the story?

Describe the setting from your major characters POV.

Protagonist: Antagonist:

○   ○

○   ○

○   ○

Touch:

Taste:

Sight:

Smell:

Sound:

Scene
Worksheet

View point character:

POV:

Other characters:

Time:

Setting:

How will this scene advance the story?:

What is the view point characters goal?:

What is the source of conflict?:*(What's stopping the character achieving their goal?)*

What is the dramatic ending?:*(Are you leaving the reader hanging with suspense?)*

What is the sequel?: *(Decide what to do next, oscillate scenes between fast and slow pace.)*

Scene
Worksheet

View point character:

POV:

Other characters:

Time:

Setting:

How will this scene advance the story?:

What is the view point characters goal?:

What is the source of conflict?: *(What's stopping the character achieving their goal?)*

What is the dramatic ending?: *(Are you leaving the reader hanging with suspense?)*

What is the sequel?: *(Decide what to do next, oscillate scenes between fast and slow pace.)*

Scene
Worksheet

View point character:

POV:

Other characters:

Time:

Setting:

How will this scene advance the story?:

What is the view point characters goal?:

What is the source of conflict?:(*What's stopping the character achieving their goal?*)

What is the dramatic ending?:(*Are you leaving the reader hanging with suspense?*)

What is the sequel?: (*Decide what to do next, oscillate scenes between fast and slow pace.*)

Scene
Worksheet

View point character:

POV:

Other characters:

Time:

Setting:

How will this scene advance the story?:

What is the view point characters goal?:

What is the source of conflict?: *(What's stopping the character achieving their goal?)*

What is the dramatic ending?: *(Are you leaving the reader hanging with suspense?)*

What is the sequel?: *(Decide what to do next, oscillate scenes between fast and slow pace.)*

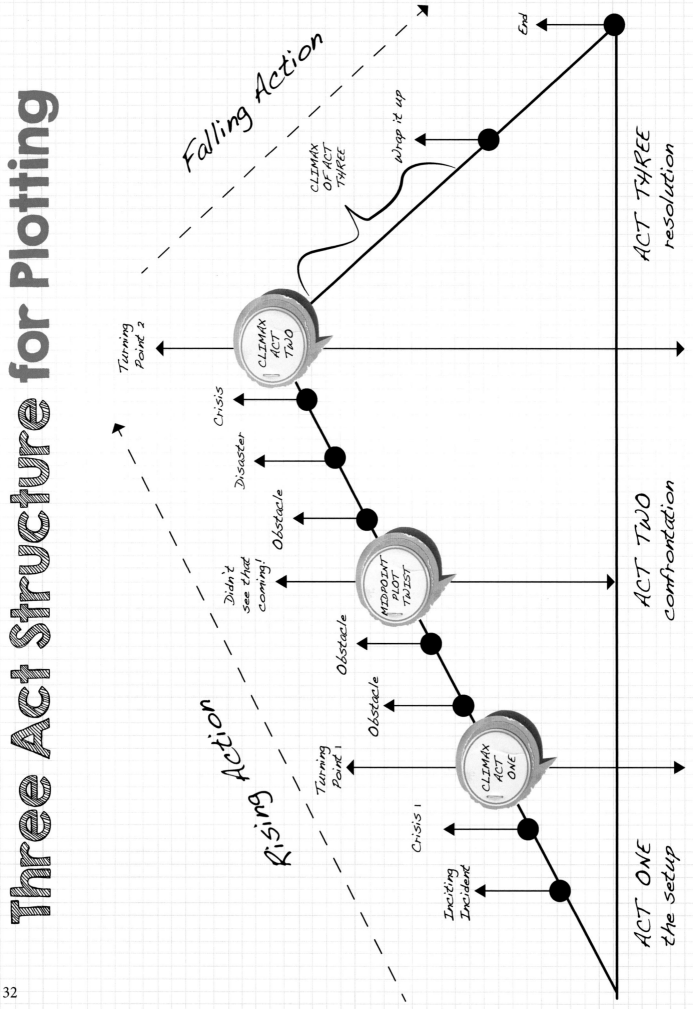

Three Act Structure for Plotting

Falling Action

Rising Action

CLIMAX OF ACT THREE

Wrap it up

End

Turning Point 2

Crisis

Disaster

Obstacle

Didn't see that coming!

CLIMAX ACT TWO

Obstacle

MIDPOINT PLOT TWIST

Obstacle

Obstacle

Turning Point 1

Crisis 1

CLIMAX ACT ONE

Inciting Incident

ACT ONE
the setup

ACT TWO
confrontation

ACT THREE
resolution

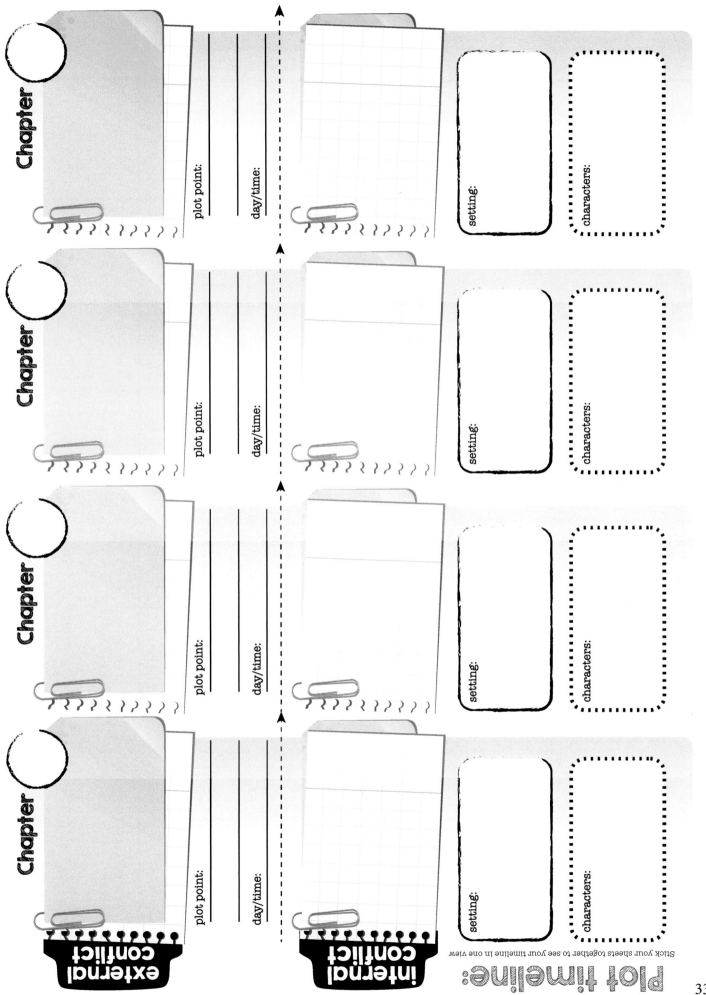

Chapter ◯

Chapter ◯

Chapter ◯

Chapter ◯

plot point: _____

day/time:

setting:

characters:

external conflict

internal conflict

Plot timeline:

Stick your sheets together to see your timeline in one view

33

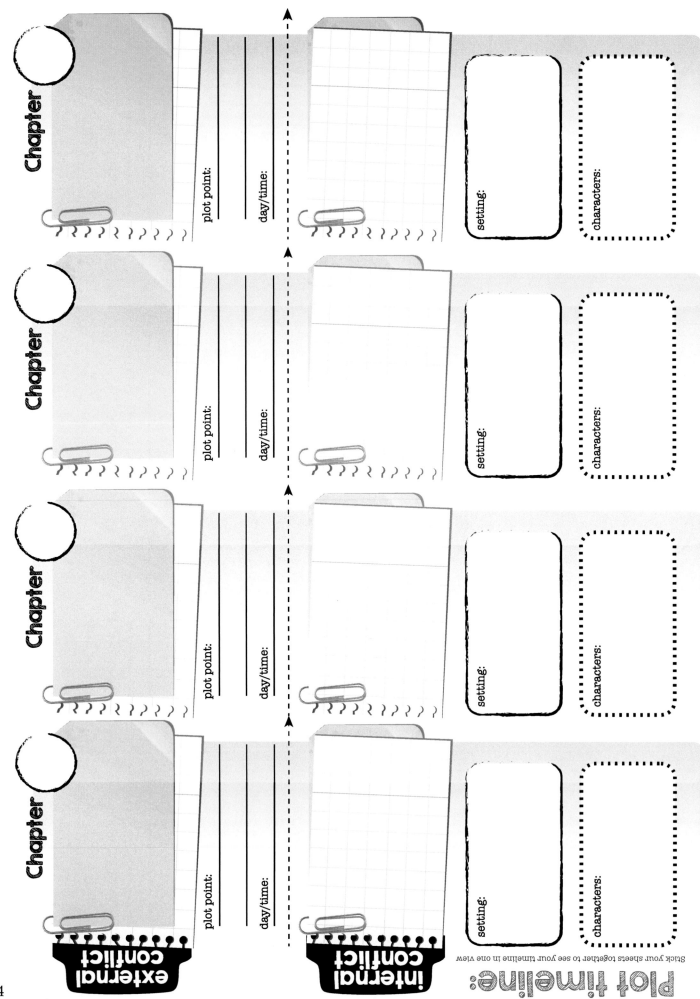

Chapter ◯

plot point: _____

day/time: _____

setting:

characters:

Chapter ◯

plot point: _____

day/time: _____

setting:

characters:

Chapter ◯

plot point: _____

day/time: _____

setting:

characters:

Chapter ◯

plot point: _____

day/time: _____

setting:

characters:

external conflict

internal conflict

Plot timeline:

Stick your sheets together to see your timeline in one view.

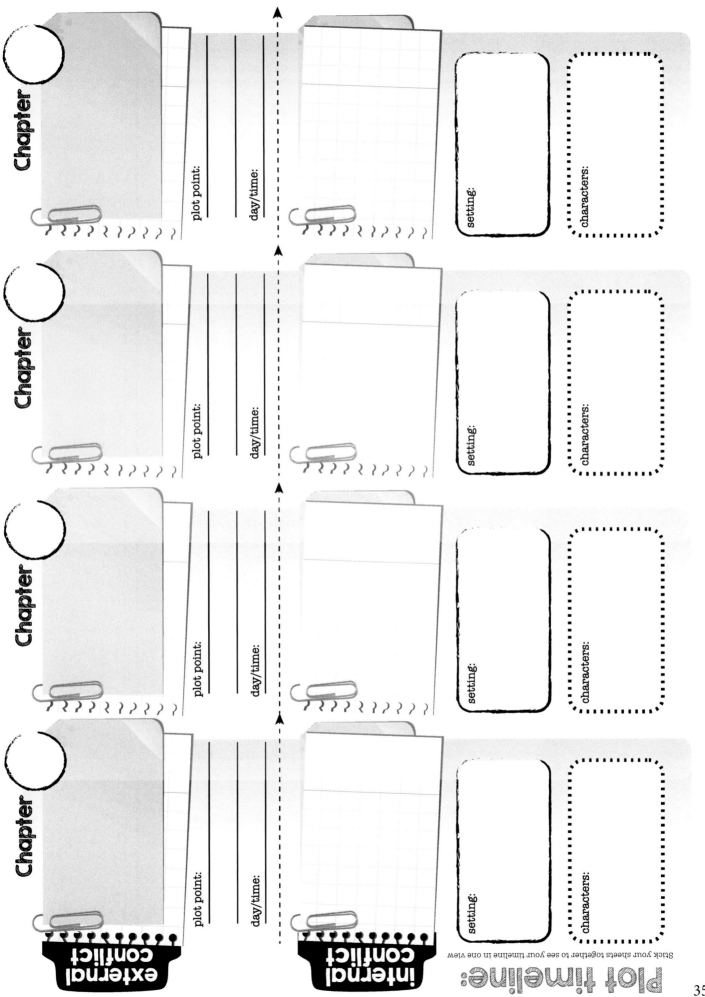

Chapter ◯

plot point: _____

day/time: _____

setting:

characters:

Chapter ◯

plot point: _____

day/time: _____

setting:

characters:

Chapter ◯

plot point: _____

day/time: _____

setting:

characters:

Chapter ◯

plot point: _____

day/time: _____

external conflict

internal conflict

setting:

characters:

Plot timeline:

Stick your sheets together to see your timeline in one view

35

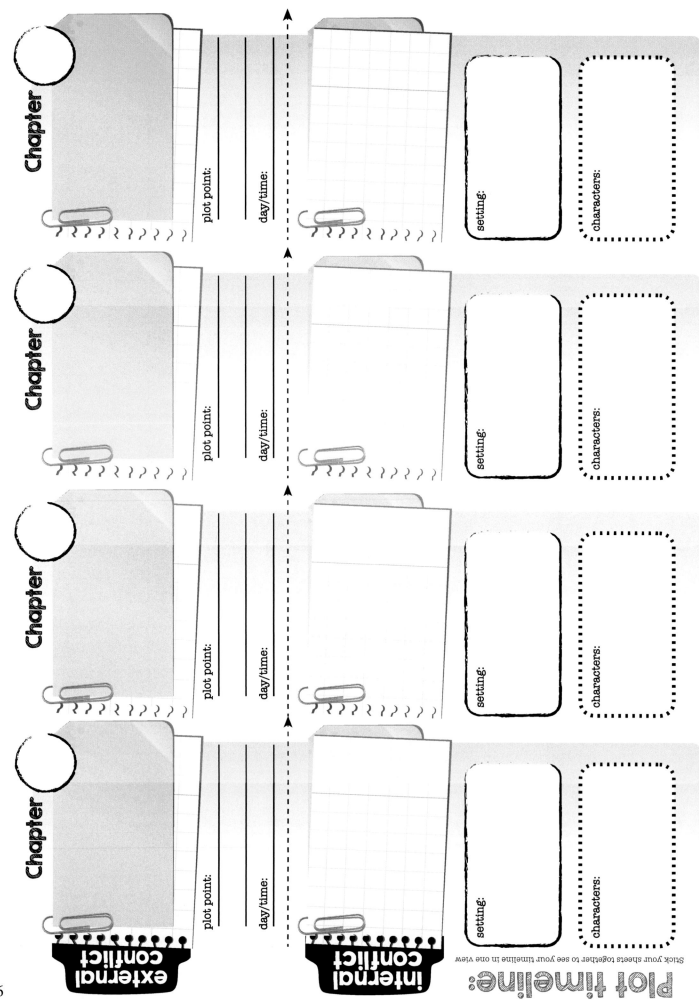

Chapter ⬭

plot point:

day/time:

setting:

characters:

external conflict

Chapter ⬭

plot point:

day/time:

setting:

characters:

Chapter ⬭

plot point:

day/time:

setting:

characters:

Chapter ⬭

plot point:

day/time:

setting:

characters:

internal conflict

Plot timeline:

Stick your sheets together to see your timeline in one view

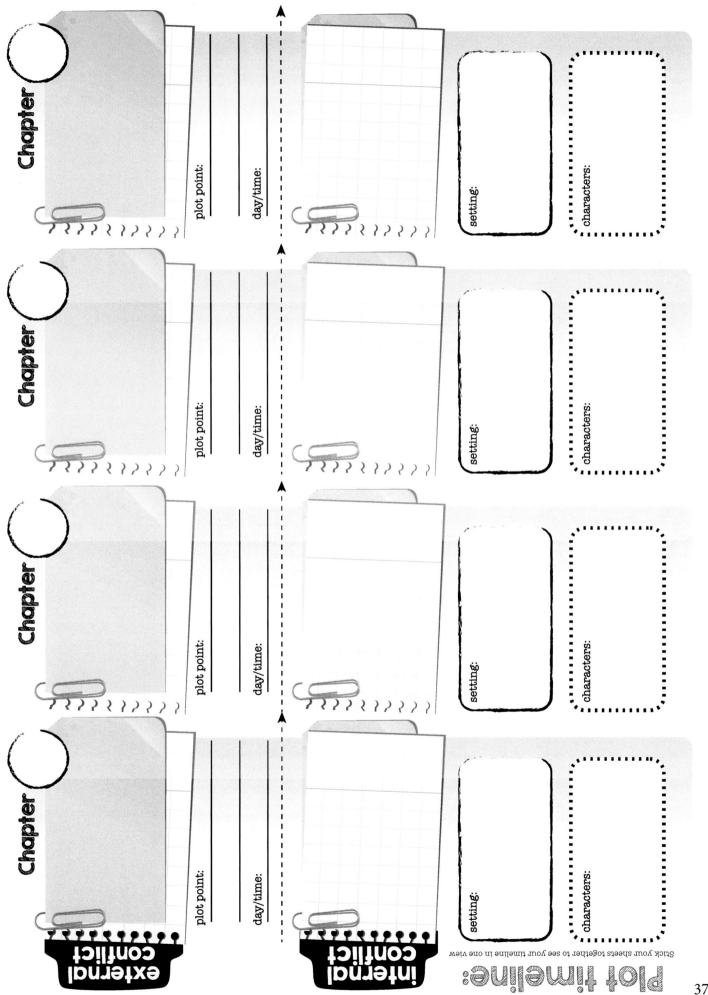

Chapter ◯

plot point: ___

day/time: ___

setting:

characters:

Chapter ◯

plot point: ___

day/time: ___

setting:

characters:

Chapter ◯

plot point: ___

day/time: ___

setting:

characters:

Chapter ◯

plot point: ___

day/time: ___

setting:

characters:

external conflict

internal conflict

Plot timeline:

Stick your sheets together to see your timeline in one view

37

Notes

Notes

Sticky note Plotting

Do you prefer to plot using sticky notes? Use this worksheet to affix your notes, move the plot points and scenes around before sticking them in permanently for safe keeping.

Do you prefer to plot using sticky notes? Use this worksheet to affix your notes, move the plot points and scenes around before sticking them in permanently for safe keeping.

Sticky note Plotting

Do you prefer to plot using sticky notes? Use this worksheet to affix your notes, move the plot points and scenes around before sticking them in permanently for safe keeping.

Sticky note Plotting

Do you prefer to plot using sticky notes? Use this worksheet to affix your notes, move the plot points and scenes around before sticking them in permanently for safe keeping.

Sticky note Plotting

Do you prefer to plot using sticky notes? Use this worksheet to affix your notes, move the plot points and scenes around before sticking them in permanently for safe keeping.

Sticky note Plotting

Do you prefer to plot using sticky notes? Use this worksheet to affix your notes, move the plot points and scenes around before sticking them in permanently for safe keeping.

Best lines
from your best authors

Learn from your favorite authors. Record the best lines from books, movies or anywhere else to inspire you when writing your own novel.

Line	Source

Best lines
from your best authors

Learn from your favorite authors. Record the best lines from books, movies or anywhere else to inspire you when writing your own novel.

Line	Source

Plot Time-line Tracker

Chapter	Scene	Time / Day	Location	POV	Characters	Notes

Plot Time-line Tracker

Chapter	Scene	Time / Day	Location	POV	Characters	Notes

Research Notes

Story Title: _____

Research needed:

	✓

Fact Checking List:

Chapter	Pages	Fact	✓

Research Notes

Story Title: _____

Research needed:

	✓

Fact Checking List:

Chapter	Pages	Fact	✓

Show - don't tell - emotions
Writing exercise

Use this worksheet to practise showing how to write emotions. Show by explaining the body language. Keep the pages as a quick reference guide for your writing.

Emotion	Tell	Show
	Anger	E.g. Flared nostrils, pointing finger, punching or kicking ...
	Boredom	
	Confusion	
	Disgust	
	Disbelief	

Show - don't tell - emotions
Writing exercise

Use this worksheet to practise showing how to write emotions. Show by explaining the body language.
Keep the pages as a quick reference guide for your writing.

Emotion	Tell	Show
	Fatigue	
	Fear	
	Grief	
	Happy	
	Surprise	

Show - don't tell - emotions
Writing exercise

Use this worksheet to practise showing how to write emotions.
Keep the pages as a quick reference guide for your writing.

Emotion	Tell	Show

Show - don't tell - emotions
Writing exercise

Use this worksheet to practise showing how to write emotions.
Keep the pages as a quick reference guide for your writing.

Emotion	Tell	Show

Just keep writing
Editing notes

Don't waste time or your precious mojo going back to change bits of your first draft.
Record your intended changes here, and use it as a reference for when you are editing.

Chapter	Pages	Description of changes needed

Just keep writing
Editing notes

Don't waste time or your precious mojo going back to change bits of your first draft.
Record your intended changes here, and use it as a reference for when you are editing.

Chapter	Pages	Description of changes needed

Editing Stage I

Before you re-read Draft 1

1. Go through your first draft and action the notes from your 'just keep writing' worksheet.
2. Check your plot time lines, character trackers and scene trackers to make sure everything is in chronological order.
3. Now that you've had a think about it? Is there anything you'd like to change in your novel before you start reading the first draft – chapters you need to delete, or plot points you aren't happy with? Write it down below, then action the changes.
4. Leave the draft for at least two weeks before you print it out in hard copy and read through it cover to cover.

Last minute first draft changes

Characters:

Scenes:

Plot points:

Conflict:

Theme:

Random notes:

Editing Stage 2

1. You've made your last minute changes and have now printed out your first draft on paper. One sided, double spacing with at least 1 inch margins.
2. It's been at least 2 weeks since you made those stage 1 changes, grab a coffee, sit down and start reading. Don't stop except to make minor continuity notes in the margin.
3. The aim of the game here is to pretend you are the reader and get an overall, general feel for your book.
4. Think about:
   - Plot holes (highlight any areas that are missing information)
   - Do you get bored (highlight boring bits and just write 'bored' next to it)
   - Are any words awkward to read? (Grab a highlighter and just write 'awkward')

   WHATEVER YOU DO, DON'T TAKE LONGER THAN A FEW SECONDS TO MAKE NOTES.

Answer these questions once you have finished reading your book, and then make appropriate changes on your digital manuscript according to your notes.

Was the opening compelling? At what point did you stop reading?

_____

_____

Did you get bored at any point, or were any characters boring?

_____

_____

Did your main character have an ARC? (Did they learn, or change something as a result of the story?)

_____

_____

Was the setting vivid enough without being to wordy? (Did you show, not tell?)

_____

_____

Did your plot make sense? (Were there any inconsistencies, or discrepancies, was it believable?)

_____

_____

Was the ending satisfying? (Did you tie up all loose ends?)

_____

_____

Editing Stage 3

You've made all of your major changes to the structure, now its time to look at your writing style with a fine tooth comb.

1. Are you using ACTIVE VOICE?
   Do a search on your word processor for the words 'was', 'were', 'to be' and work out if the sentence needs adjusting - if you need help, Google 'identifying passive voice'.
2. Have you got too many ADVERBS?
   Do a search on your word processor for words ending in 'ly' and change appropriately.
3. CUT, CUT, CUT.
   - If it's obvious, cut it. E.g. I don't need to know he picked up a cup with his hand – that's obvious. Just say he picked up a cup.
   - If you read the words aloud and they sound awkward, cut it.
   - If you are repeating yourself, cut it.
   - If you have a cliche, cut it - find another way to say what you want.
   - If you have a long sentence, cut it, or split it into smaller sentences, (especially in fast paced areas of writing). Keep it simple.
4. Search for these QUALIFIERS
   'very', 'often', 'hopefully', 'practically', 'basically', 'really', 'mostly' - Most of these words can be cut to help tighten your writing style.

Research your own editing tips, write them down below.

Editing Stage 4

You've made it to the final stage - grammar, punctuation and spelling. Print out your manuscript again. Use the following marks in red pen as you read and correct.

∧ Insert a word, letter or phrase.

✗ Delete.

≡ Capitalize.

/ Change to lower case.

⊙ Insert a period.

∧ Insert a comma.

∨ Insert apostrophe.

∨∨ Insert quotation marks.

Insert space.

⌒ Close up space.

⌒ Transpose.

¶ New paragraph.

SP Check spelling

— Replace

Tip

Consider hiring a freelance editor, you can usually find a list at your state writing center's website.

Tip

Don't rely on spell check. Get someone to help you proof your manuscript. If you have no one, try online applications, many are FREE!

Notes

Wooden Character
Checker

Check these tips to see if your characters stack up, or are they plain boring?

Show the bad as well as the good, just make it interesting.

Have you got inside their head?

Showed enough thoughts, internal sensations, feelings?

Is your character a cliche?

Has your character changed because of the conflict in the book?

How is their dialogue? Does it reveal parts about their personality, not only the plot?

Have you remembered to describe them adequately?

Do their actions coincide with their personal traits?

Everybody wants something in life, what do they WANT?

What's their 'out of character' behaviour?

Do they have a distinguishing quirk? Perhaps a particular word, or action that makes them stand out.

Can you see their internal conflict come through in their appearance? (e.g. scruffy clothes for someone depressed.)

Contrast their inner thoughts with immediate dialogue

What do other people say about them?

People will forget what you said, people will forget what you did,

but people will never forget how you made them feel.

- Maya Angelou

Author Bio

Name:

Place of birth/home town:

What do you do for a living?

Past written works:

Relevant education:

Awards:

Quirky habit:

Stand out fact:

Contact Info:

Agent Contact:

Other:

Affix
photo
here

Story Synopsis

A synopsis is a summary of your story. You need to be specific, and leave out the marketing sales pitch. This is where you put in your outline if you have it. Keep it to one page (typed), keep it simple, write in the third person even if your book is in the first. Don't forget to add the ending. Spoilers are allowed. This is what goes to the agent or publisher if you are trying the traditional publishing route.

About the book

What is your 'Elevator Pitch'? This is the 30 second spiel you give when someone asks what your book is about. Fill out the below worksheet to break your story down.

1. In the beginning ...

2. Every day ...

3. Until one day ...

4. Because of that ...

5. Because of that ...

6. Until finally ...

Re-write to fit into this box.

Book Cover Research

Use this page to stick samples of book covers in your chosen genre.
Note the similar elements.

My genre:

Similar Elements (Popular colours, fonts, subject matter etc)

Book Cover Sketch - Front

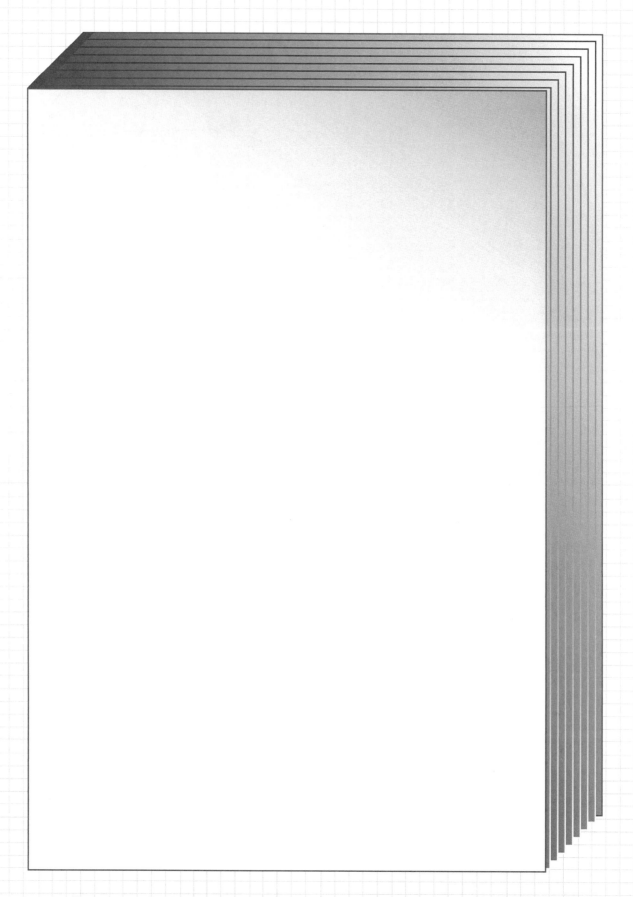

Give to your book cover designer to help them understand what you want.

Book Cover Sketch - Back

Publisher Contacts

Write down all of the publishing contacts you've sourced here. Use a highlighter to show who you've contacted.

Name	Company	Email	Phone	Website	Address

Agent Contacts

Write down all of the Agent contacts you've sourced here. Use a highlighter to show who you've contacted.

Name	Company	Email	Phone	Website	Address

limp
pithy
pulpy
satiny
silken
coarse
stiff
strong
firm
sharp
barbed
horned
itch
throb
grainy

mirrorlike
flush
even
uniform
frictionless
porous
rubbery
springy
elastic
supple
wobbly
stirring
charged
stimulating
electrifying
arousing
energizing
hair raising
vibes
tingles

burning
curious
eerie
prickling
stinging
strange
tingling
spongy
gritty
jagged
soft
smooth
hard
slick
prickly
bristly
fluffy
furry
hairy
wiry
leafy

blazing
sizzling
hot
warm
cold
dusty
rough
abrasive
crumbly
lumpy
powdery
sandy
scratchy
tufted
woolly
uruly
stiff
silky

blistering
broiling
burning
feverish
fiery
flaming
parching
roasting
scalding
stuffy
stale
humid
fetid
muggy
stagnant
airy
breezy
rumpled
feathery

arctic
cool
dry
freezing
calm
frosty
glacial
nippy
delicate
creamy
elastic
flexible
mushy
pliable
supple
thin
velvety
cottony
cushiony
doughy
flabby
fleshy
fluid
formless
gelatinou
pointy
serrated
spiked
splintery
thorny
glassy

Touchy feely words

intolerant

needlelike

malleable

scorching

suffocating

sweltering

words that describe someone's voice

breathy
adjective
with loud breathing noises

thin
adjective
a thin voice or sound is high and unpleasant to listen to

brittle
adjective
if you speak in a brittle voice, you sound as if you are about to cry

appealing
adjective
an appealing look, voice etc shows that you want help, approval, or agreement

dead
adjective
if someone's eyes are dead, or if their voice is dead, they feel or show no emotion

fruity
adjective
a fruity voice or laugh is deep and strong in a pleasant way

gruff
adjective
a gruff voice has a rough low sound

gravelly
adjective
a gravelly voice sounds low and rough

croaky
adjective
if someone's voice sounds croaky, they speak in a low rough voice that sounds as if they have a sore throat

disembodied
adjective
a disembodied voice comes from someone who you cannot see

small
adjective
a small voice or sound is quiet

hoarse
adjective
someone who is hoarse or has a hoarse voice speaks in a low rough voice

high-pitched
adjective
a high-pitched voice or sound is very high

adenoidal
adjective
if someone's voice is adenoidal, some of the sound seems to come through their nose

monotonous
adjective
a monotonous sound or voice is boring and unpleasant because it does not change in loudness or become higher or lower

husky
adjective
a husky voice is deep and sounds hoarse , often in an attractive way

flat
adjective
spoken in a voice that does not go up and down

guttural
adjective
a guttural sound is deep and made at the back of your throat

low
adjective
a low voice or sound is quiet and difficult to hear or deep sounding

nasal
adjective
someone with a nasal voice sounds as if they are speaking through their nose

raucous
adjective
a raucous voice or noise is loud and sounds rough

orotund
adjective
an orotund voice is loud and clear

honeyed
adjective
honeyed words sound very nice but you cannot trust the person who is speaking

penetrating
adjective
a penetrating voice or sound is so high or loud that it makes you slightly uncomfortable

rough
adjective
a rough voice is not soft and is unpleasant to listen to

grating
adjective
a grating voice, laugh, or sound is unpleasant and annoying

silvery
adjective
a silvery voice or sound is clear, light, and pleasant

ringing
adjective
a ringing sound or voice is very loud and clear

shrill
adjective
a shrill noise or voice is very loud, high, and unpleasant

smoky
adjective
a smoky voice or smoky eyes are sexually attractive in a slightly mysterious way

strident
adjective
a strident voice or sound is loud and unpleasant

singsong
adjective
if you speak in a singsong voice, your voice rises and falls in a musical way

quietly
adverb
in a quiet voice

taut
adjective
used about something such as a voice or expression that shows someone is nervous or angry

plummy
adjective
a plummy voice or way of speaking is considered to be typical of an English person of a high social class. This word shows that you dislike people who speak like this.

strangled
adjective
a strangled sound is one that someone stops before they finish making it

thick
adjective
if your voice is thick with an emotion, it sounds less clear than usual because of the emotion

matter-of-fact
adjective
used about someone's behaviour or voice

wheezy
adjective
a wheezy noise sounds as if it is made by someone who has difficulty breathing

throaty
adjective
a throaty sound is low and seems to come from deep in your throat

tight
adjective
a tight voice or expression shows that you are nervous or annoyed

tremulous
adjective
it is not steady, for example because you are afraid or excited

wobbly
adjective
if your voice is wobbly, it goes up and down, usually because you are frightened, not confident, or are going to cry

Source:http://www.macmillandictionary.com/thesaurus-category/british/Words-used-to-describe-someone-s-voice

lay eye's on

Feast one's eyes

bug out
if someone's eyes bug out, they open very wide, for example because the person is shocked by something

pout
to push out your lips in order to look more sexually attractive

suck your teeth
to pull your lips together when you are thinking about something or feel doubt about it

wink
to quickly close an open one eye as a sign to someone, for example a sign tha what you have jus said is a joke or a secret

furrow
if your brow furrows, or if you furrow it, deep lines appear on your forehead, for example because you are concentrating or worrying

curl your lip
to pull your top lip upwards at one side in a way that shows that you are annoyed, bored, or do not respect someone

screw up
if you screw up your face, pull your forehead down push your mouth and n up, usually to show that dislike something

scowl
to twist your face into an expression that shows you are angry

glower
to look angrily at someone

INSTEAD OF 'LOOK' USE

Stare	Attention	Eye	Glance	Glimpse	Peek
Review	View	Behold	Case	Cast	Contemplation
Flash	Gander	Gaze	Gun	Inspection	Introspection
Leer	Marking	Noticing	Observation	Once-over	Reconnaissance
Regard	Regarding	Scrutiny	Sight	Slant	Speculation
Squint	Surveillance	Survey	Swivel	Viewing	Evil eye
Keeping watch	Look-see	Disregard	Ignore	Neglect	Address
Regard	Judge	Sneer	Grimace	Simper	Smirk
Pout	Smile	Scowl	Glower	Frown	Beam
Bore	Eyeball	Focus	Get a load of	Get an eyeful	Give the eye
Glare	Gloat	Goggle	Look	Ogle	Peer
Rubberneck	Size up	Take in	Wonder	Yawp	Scrutiny
Watch	Seeing	Admire	Contemplate	Inspect	Look fixedly
Moon	Observe	Peep	Pin	Pipe	Size up
Glimpse	Shine	Trace	Twinkle	Glitter	Glimmer
Scowl	Sulk	Look daggers	Gloom	Audit	Check
Examine	Explore	Hunt	Inspect	Supervise	Note
Baby-sit	Ensure	Leer	Rivet	Blink	Snatch
Have a gander	Spy	Discover	Grasp	Sense	Zero in
Delve	Inquire	Investigate	Probe	Sift	Search
Consider	Leaf through	Riffle	Study	Sweep	Take stock of
Comb	Ferret	Forage	Frisk	Grope	Poke into
Pry	Quest	Rake	Ransack	Rummage	Scan
Detect	Distinguish	Heed	Make out	Notice	Recognize
Spot	Witness	Resemble	Indicate	Glaze	Mope
Stalk	Do a slow burn	Cloud up	Look askance		

Change the way you 'GO'
words to use instead of 'go', 'went' or 'walk'

flee	hie	get off	bolted	scurried	sashayed
fly	hightail	hit the road	bounced	scuttled	sauntered
leave	journey	make a break for it	capered	set out	scooted
move	lam	make one's way	chugged	skidded	whisked
pass	mosey	move out	clambered	skirted	waddled
progress	quit	pull out	crawled	slid	ventured
retire	split	push off	inched	slinked	veered
travel	vamoose	run along	jumped	slogged	vaulted
abscond	withdraw	run away	leapt	fell	trudged
approach	beat it	set off	left	trailed	scaled
cruise	bug out	shove off	legged it	traipsed	wriggled
depart	get away	advanced	journeyed	traveled	zipped
escape	get going	ambled	lunged	trekked	zoomed
exit	get lost	approached	marched	gallivanted	skip out
fare	scram	bounded	meandered	hopped	evacuate
begone	drift	jaunt	pass	skedaddle	slip away
make oneself scarce		navigate	proceed	wander	vanish

75

Monthly
writing planner

M	T	W	Th
W/C goal: W/C actual:	W/C goal: W/C actual:	W/C goal: W/C actual:	W/C goal: W/C actual:
W/C goal: W/C actual:	W/C goal: W/C actual:	W/C goal: W/C actual:	W/C goal: W/C actual:
W/C goal: W/C actual:	W/C goal: W/C actual:	W/C goal: W/C actual:	W/C goal: W/C actual:
W/C goal: W/C actual:	W/C goal: W/C actual:	W/C goal: W/C actual:	W/C goal: W/C actual:
W/C goal: W/C actual:	W/C goal: W/C actual:	W/C goal: W/C actual:	W/C goal: W/C actual:
W/C goal: W/C actual:	W/C goal: W/C actual:	W/C goal: W/C actual:	W/C goal: W/C actual:

Weekly W/C goal:

....

Daily W/C goal:

....

For the month of:

F	S	Su	To-Do Research, write, Brainstorm etc
◯ W/C goal: W/C actual:	◯ W/C goal: W/C actual:	◯ W/C goal: W/C actual:	☐ ☐ ☐
◯ W/C goal: W/C actual:	◯ W/C goal: W/C actual:	◯ W/C goal: W/C actual:	☐ ☐ ☐
◯ W/C goal: W/C actual:	◯ W/C goal: W/C actual:	◯ W/C goal: W/C actual:	☐ ☐ ☐
◯ W/C goal: W/C actual:	◯ W/C goal: W/C actual:	◯ W/C goal: W/C actual:	☐ ☐ ☐
◯ W/C goal: W/C actual:	◯ W/C goal: W/C actual:	◯ W/C goal: W/C actual:	☐ ☐ ☐
◯ W/C goal: W/C actual:	◯ W/C goal: W/C actual:	◯ W/C goal: W/C actual:	☐ ☐ ☐

Monthly
writing planner

M	T	W	Th
◯	◯	◯	◯
W/C goal: W/C actual:	W/C goal: W/C actual:	W/C goal: W/C actual:	W/C goal: W/C actual:
◯	◯	◯	◯
W/C goal: W/C actual:	W/C goal: W/C actual:	W/C goal: W/C actual:	W/C goal: W/C actual:
◯	◯	◯	◯
W/C goal: W/C actual:	W/C goal: W/C actual:	W/C goal: W/C actual:	W/C goal: W/C actual:
◯	◯	◯	◯
W/C goal: W/C actual:	W/C goal: W/C actual:	W/C goal: W/C actual:	W/C goal: W/C actual:
◯	◯	◯	◯
W/C goal: W/C actual:	W/C goal: W/C actual:	W/C goal: W/C actual:	W/C goal: W/C actual:
◯	◯	◯	◯
W/C goal: W/C actual:	W/C goal: W/C actual:	W/C goal: W/C actual:	W/C goal: W/C actual:

Weekly W/C goal:

....

Daily W/C goal:

....

For the month of:

F	S	Su	To-Do Research, write, Brainstorm etc
◯ W/C goal: W/C actual:	◯ W/C goal: W/C actual:	◯ W/C goal: W/C actual:	☐ ☐ ☐
◯ W/C goal: W/C actual:	◯ W/C goal: W/C actual:	◯ W/C goal: W/C actual:	☐ ☐ ☐
◯ W/C goal: W/C actual:	◯ W/C goal: W/C actual:	◯ W/C goal: W/C actual:	☐ ☐ ☐
◯ W/C goal: W/C actual:	◯ W/C goal: W/C actual:	◯ W/C goal: W/C actual:	☐ ☐ ☐
◯ W/C goal: W/C actual:	◯ W/C goal: W/C actual:	◯ W/C goal: W/C actual:	☐ ☐ ☐
◯ W/C goal: W/C actual:	◯ W/C goal: W/C actual:	◯ W/C goal: W/C actual:	☐ ☐ ☐

Monthly
writing planner

Actual Monthly W/C:

M	T	W	Th
W/C goal: W/C actual:	W/C goal: W/C actual:	W/C goal: W/C actual:	W/C goal: W/C actual:
W/C goal: W/C actual:	W/C goal: W/C actual:	W/C goal: W/C actual:	W/C goal: W/C actual:
W/C goal: W/C actual:	W/C goal: W/C actual:	W/C goal: W/C actual:	W/C goal: W/C actual:
W/C goal: W/C actual:	W/C goal: W/C actual:	W/C goal: W/C actual:	W/C goal: W/C actual:
W/C goal: W/C actual:	W/C goal: W/C actual:	W/C goal: W/C actual:	W/C goal: W/C actual:
W/C goal: W/C actual:	W/C goal: W/C actual:	W/C goal: W/C actual:	W/C goal: W/C actual:

Weekly W/C goal:

....

Daily W/C goal:

....

For the month of:

F	S	Su	To-Do
			Research, write, Brainstorm etc
◯	◯	◯	☐ ☐ ☐
W/C goal: W/C actual:	W/C goal: W/C actual:	W/C goal: W/C actual:	
◯	◯	◯	☐ ☐ ☐
W/C goal: W/C actual:	W/C goal: W/C actual:	W/C goal: W/C actual:	
◯	◯	◯	☐ ☐ ☐
W/C goal: W/C actual:	W/C goal: W/C actual:	W/C goal: W/C actual:	
◯	◯	◯	☐ ☐ ☐
W/C goal: W/C actual:	W/C goal: W/C actual:	W/C goal: W/C actual:	
◯	◯	◯	☐ ☐ ☐
W/C goal: W/C actual:	W/C goal: W/C actual:	W/C goal: W/C actual:	
◯	◯	◯	☐ ☐ ☐
W/C goal: W/C actual:	W/C goal: W/C actual:	W/C goal: W/C actual:	

Monthly
writing planner

Monthly Word Count (W/C) goal:
....

Actual Monthly W/C:
....

M	T	W	Th
○	○	○	○
W/C goal: W/C actual:	W/C goal: W/C actual:	W/C goal: W/C actual:	W/C goal: W/C actual:
○	○	○	○
W/C goal: W/C actual:	W/C goal: W/C actual:	W/C goal: W/C actual:	W/C goal: W/C actual:
○	○	○	○
W/C goal: W/C actual:	W/C goal: W/C actual:	W/C goal: W/C actual:	W/C goal: W/C actual:
○	○	○	○
W/C goal: W/C actual:	W/C goal: W/C actual:	W/C goal: W/C actual:	W/C goal: W/C actual:
○	○	○	○
W/C goal: W/C actual:	W/C goal: W/C actual:	W/C goal: W/C actual:	W/C goal: W/C actual:
○	○	○	○
W/C goal: W/C actual:	W/C goal: W/C actual:	W/C goal: W/C actual:	W/C goal: W/C actual:

Weekly W/C goal:

. . . .

Daily W/C goal:

. . . .

For the month of:

F	S	Su	To-Do
			Research, write, Brainstorm etc
◯	◯	◯	☐ ☐ ☐
W/C goal: W/C actual:	W/C goal: W/C actual:	W/C goal: W/C actual:	
◯	◯	◯	☐ ☐ ☐
W/C goal: W/C actual:	W/C goal: W/C actual:	W/C goal: W/C actual:	
◯	◯	◯	☐ ☐ ☐
W/C goal: W/C actual:	W/C goal: W/C actual:	W/C goal: W/C actual:	
◯	◯	◯	☐ ☐ ☐
W/C goal: W/C actual:	W/C goal: W/C actual:	W/C goal: W/C actual:	
◯	◯	◯	☐ ☐ ☐
W/C goal: W/C actual:	W/C goal: W/C actual:	W/C goal: W/C actual:	
◯	◯	◯	☐ ☐ ☐
W/C goal: W/C actual:	W/C goal: W/C actual:	W/C goal: W/C actual:	

Monthly
writing planner

M	T	W	Th
W/C goal: W/C actual:	W/C goal: W/C actual:	W/C goal: W/C actual:	W/C goal: W/C actual:
W/C goal: W/C actual:	W/C goal: W/C actual:	W/C goal: W/C actual:	W/C goal: W/C actual:
W/C goal: W/C actual:	W/C goal: W/C actual:	W/C goal: W/C actual:	W/C goal: W/C actual:
W/C goal: W/C actual:	W/C goal: W/C actual:	W/C goal: W/C actual:	W/C goal: W/C actual:
W/C goal: W/C actual:	W/C goal: W/C actual:	W/C goal: W/C actual:	W/C goal: W/C actual:
W/C goal: W/C actual:	W/C goal: W/C actual:	W/C goal: W/C actual:	W/C goal: W/C actual:

Weekly W/C goal:

. . . .

Daily W/C goal:

. . . .

For the month of:

F	S	Su	To-Do Research, write, Brainstorm etc
○ W/C goal: W/C actual:	○ W/C goal: W/C actual:	○ W/C goal: W/C actual:	☐ ☐ ☐
○ W/C goal: W/C actual:	○ W/C goal: W/C actual:	○ W/C goal: W/C actual:	☐ ☐ ☐
○ W/C goal: W/C actual:	○ W/C goal: W/C actual:	○ W/C goal: W/C actual:	☐ ☐ ☐
○ W/C goal: W/C actual:	○ W/C goal: W/C actual:	○ W/C goal: W/C actual:	☐ ☐ ☐
○ W/C goal: W/C actual:	○ W/C goal: W/C actual:	○ W/C goal: W/C actual:	☐ ☐ ☐
○ W/C goal: W/C actual:	○ W/C goal: W/C actual:	○ W/C goal: W/C actual:	☐ ☐ ☐

Monthly
writing planner

M	T	W	Th
◯	◯	◯	◯
W/C goal: W/C actual:	W/C goal: W/C actual:	W/C goal: W/C actual:	W/C goal: W/C actual:
◯	◯	◯	◯
W/C goal: W/C actual:	W/C goal: W/C actual:	W/C goal: W/C actual:	W/C goal: W/C actual:
◯	◯	◯	◯
W/C goal: W/C actual:	W/C goal: W/C actual:	W/C goal: W/C actual:	W/C goal: W/C actual:
◯	◯	◯	◯
W/C goal: W/C actual:	W/C goal: W/C actual:	W/C goal: W/C actual:	W/C goal: W/C actual:
◯	◯	◯	◯
W/C goal: W/C actual:	W/C goal: W/C actual:	W/C goal: W/C actual:	W/C goal: W/C actual:
◯	◯	◯	◯
W/C goal: W/C actual:	W/C goal: W/C actual:	W/C goal: W/C actual:	W/C goal: W/C actual:

Weekly W/C goal:

....

Daily W/C goal:

....

For the month of:

F	S	Su	To-Do
			Research, write, Brainstorm etc
◯	◯	◯	☐ ☐ ☐
W/C goal: W/C actual:	W/C goal: W/C actual:	W/C goal: W/C actual:	
◯	◯	◯	☐ ☐ ☐
W/C goal: W/C actual:	W/C goal: W/C actual:	W/C goal: W/C actual:	
◯	◯	◯	☐ ☐ ☐
W/C goal: W/C actual:	W/C goal: W/C actual:	W/C goal: W/C actual:	
◯	◯	◯	☐ ☐ ☐
W/C goal: W/C actual:	W/C goal: W/C actual:	W/C goal: W/C actual:	
◯	◯	◯	☐ ☐ ☐
W/C goal: W/C actual:	W/C goal: W/C actual:	W/C goal: W/C actual:	
◯	◯	◯	☐ ☐ ☐
W/C goal: W/C actual:	W/C goal: W/C actual:	W/C goal: W/C actual:	

Monthly
writing planner

Monthly Word Count (W/C) goal:

....

Actual Monthly W/C:

....

M	T	W	Th
W/C goal: W/C actual:	W/C goal: W/C actual:	W/C goal: W/C actual:	W/C goal: W/C actual:
W/C goal: W/C actual:	W/C goal: W/C actual:	W/C goal: W/C actual:	W/C goal: W/C actual:
W/C goal: W/C actual:	W/C goal: W/C actual:	W/C goal: W/C actual:	W/C goal: W/C actual:
W/C goal: W/C actual:	W/C goal: W/C actual:	W/C goal: W/C actual:	W/C goal: W/C actual:
W/C goal: W/C actual:	W/C goal: W/C actual:	W/C goal: W/C actual:	W/C goal: W/C actual:

Weekly W/C goal:

....

Daily W/C goal:

....

For the month of:

F	S	Su	To-Do
			To-Do Research, write, Brainstorm etc
W/C goal: W/C actual:	W/C goal: W/C actual:	W/C goal: W/C actual:	☐ ☐ ☐
W/C goal: W/C actual:	W/C goal: W/C actual:	W/C goal: W/C actual:	☐ ☐ ☐
W/C goal: W/C actual:	W/C goal: W/C actual:	W/C goal: W/C actual:	☐ ☐ ☐
W/C goal: W/C actual:	W/C goal: W/C actual:	W/C goal: W/C actual:	☐ ☐ ☐
W/C goal: W/C actual:	W/C goal: W/C actual:	W/C goal: W/C actual:	☐ ☐ ☐
W/C goal: W/C actual:	W/C goal: W/C actual:	W/C goal: W/C actual:	☐ ☐ ☐

Monthly
writing planner

Monthly Word Count (W/C) goal:

....

Actual Monthly W/C:

....

M	T	W	Th
◯	◯	◯	◯
W/C goal: W/C actual:	W/C goal: W/C actual:	W/C goal: W/C actual:	W/C goal: W/C actual:
◯	◯	◯	◯
W/C goal: W/C actual:	W/C goal: W/C actual:	W/C goal: W/C actual:	W/C goal: W/C actual:
◯	◯	◯	◯
W/C goal: W/C actual:	W/C goal: W/C actual:	W/C goal: W/C actual:	W/C goal: W/C actual:
◯	◯	◯	◯
W/C goal: W/C actual:	W/C goal: W/C actual:	W/C goal: W/C actual:	W/C goal: W/C actual:
◯	◯	◯	◯
W/C goal: W/C actual:	W/C goal: W/C actual:	W/C goal: W/C actual:	W/C goal: W/C actual:
◯	◯	◯	◯
W/C goal: W/C actual:	W/C goal: W/C actual:	W/C goal: W/C actual:	W/C goal: W/C actual:

Weekly W/C goal:

....

Daily W/C goal:

....

For the month of:

F	S	Su	To-Do
			Research, write, Brainstorm etc
◯ W/C goal: W/C actual:	◯ W/C goal: W/C actual:	◯ W/C goal: W/C actual:	☐ ☐ ☐
◯ W/C goal: W/C actual:	◯ W/C goal: W/C actual:	◯ W/C goal: W/C actual:	☐ ☐ ☐
◯ W/C goal: W/C actual:	◯ W/C goal: W/C actual:	◯ W/C goal: W/C actual:	☐ ☐ ☐
◯ W/C goal: W/C actual:	◯ W/C goal: W/C actual:	◯ W/C goal: W/C actual:	☐ ☐ ☐
◯ W/C goal: W/C actual:	◯ W/C goal: W/C actual:	◯ W/C goal: W/C actual:	☐ ☐ ☐
◯ W/C goal: W/C actual:	◯ W/C goal: W/C actual:	◯ W/C goal: W/C actual:	☐ ☐

Monthly
writing planner

M	T	W	Th
◯	◯	◯	◯
W/C goal: W/C actual:	W/C goal: W/C actual:	W/C goal: W/C actual:	W/C goal: W/C actual:
◯	◯	◯	◯
W/C goal: W/C actual:	W/C goal: W/C actual:	W/C goal: W/C actual:	W/C goal: W/C actual:
◯	◯	◯	◯
W/C goal: W/C actual:	W/C goal: W/C actual:	W/C goal: W/C actual:	W/C goal: W/C actual:
◯	◯	◯	◯
W/C goal: W/C actual:	W/C goal: W/C actual:	W/C goal: W/C actual:	W/C goal: W/C actual:
◯	◯	◯	◯
W/C goal: W/C actual:	W/C goal: W/C actual:	W/C goal: W/C actual:	W/C goal: W/C actual:
◯	◯	◯	◯
W/C goal: W/C actual:	W/C goal: W/C actual:	W/C goal: W/C actual:	W/C goal: W/C actual:

Weekly W/C goal:

....

Daily W/C goal:

....

For the month of:

F	S	Su	To-Do Research, write, Brainstorm etc
W/C goal: W/C actual:	W/C goal: W/C actual:	W/C goal: W/C actual:	☐ ☐ ☐
W/C goal: W/C actual:	W/C goal: W/C actual:	W/C goal: W/C actual:	☐ ☐ ☐
W/C goal: W/C actual:	W/C goal: W/C actual:	W/C goal: W/C actual:	☐ ☐ ☐
W/C goal: W/C actual:	W/C goal: W/C actual:	W/C goal: W/C actual:	☐ ☐ ☐
W/C goal: W/C actual:	W/C goal: W/C actual:	W/C goal: W/C actual:	☐ ☐ ☐
W/C goal: W/C actual:	W/C goal: W/C actual:	W/C goal: W/C actual:	☐ ☐ ☐

Monthly
writing planner

M	T	W	Th
W/C goal: W/C actual:	W/C goal: W/C actual:	W/C goal: W/C actual:	W/C goal: W/C actual:
W/C goal: W/C actual:	W/C goal: W/C actual:	W/C goal: W/C actual:	W/C goal: W/C actual:
W/C goal: W/C actual:	W/C goal: W/C actual:	W/C goal: W/C actual:	W/C goal: W/C actual:
W/C goal: W/C actual:	W/C goal: W/C actual:	W/C goal: W/C actual:	W/C goal: W/C actual:
W/C goal: W/C actual:	W/C goal: W/C actual:	W/C goal: W/C actual:	W/C goal: W/C actual:
W/C goal: W/C actual:	W/C goal: W/C actual:	W/C goal: W/C actual:	W/C goal: W/C actual:

Weekly W/C goal:

....

Daily W/C goal:

....

For the month of:

F	S	Su	To-Do
			Research, write, Brainstorm etc
◯ W/C goal: W/C actual:	◯ W/C goal: W/C actual:	◯ W/C goal: W/C actual:	☐ ☐ ☐
◯ W/C goal: W/C actual:	◯ W/C goal: W/C actual:	◯ W/C goal: W/C actual:	☐ ☐ ☐
◯ W/C goal: W/C actual:	◯ W/C goal: W/C actual:	◯ W/C goal: W/C actual:	☐ ☐ ☐
◯ W/C goal: W/C actual:	◯ W/C goal: W/C actual:	◯ W/C goal: W/C actual:	☐ ☐ ☐
◯ W/C goal: W/C actual:	◯ W/C goal: W/C actual:	◯ W/C goal: W/C actual:	☐ ☐ ☐
◯ W/C goal: W/C actual:	◯ W/C goal: W/C actual:	◯ W/C goal: W/C actual:	☐ ☐ ☐

Monthly
writing planner

M	T	W	Th
W/C goal: W/C actual:	W/C goal: W/C actual:	W/C goal: W/C actual:	W/C goal: W/C actual:
W/C goal: W/C actual:	W/C goal: W/C actual:	W/C goal: W/C actual:	W/C goal: W/C actual:
W/C goal: W/C actual:	W/C goal: W/C actual:	W/C goal: W/C actual:	W/C goal: W/C actual:
W/C goal: W/C actual:	W/C goal: W/C actual:	W/C goal: W/C actual:	W/C goal: W/C actual:
W/C goal: W/C actual:	W/C goal: W/C actual:	W/C goal: W/C actual:	W/C goal: W/C actual:

Weekly W/C goal:

....

Daily W/C goal:

....

For the month of:

F	S	Su	To-Do Research, write, Brainstorm etc
◯ W/C goal: W/C actual:	◯ W/C goal: W/C actual:	◯ W/C goal: W/C actual:	☐ ☐ ☐
◯ W/C goal: W/C actual:	◯ W/C goal: W/C actual:	◯ W/C goal: W/C actual:	☐ ☐ ☐
◯ W/C goal: W/C actual:	◯ W/C goal: W/C actual:	◯ W/C goal: W/C actual:	☐ ☐ ☐
◯ W/C goal: W/C actual:	◯ W/C goal: W/C actual:	◯ W/C goal: W/C actual:	☐ ☐ ☐
◯ W/C goal: W/C actual:	◯ W/C goal: W/C actual:	◯ W/C goal: W/C actual:	☐ ☐ ☐
◯ W/C goal: W/C actual:	◯ W/C goal: W/C actual:	◯ W/C goal: W/C actual:	☐ ☐ ☐

Monthly
writing planner

Monthly Word Count (W/C) goal:

. . . .

Actual Monthly W/C:

. . . .

M	T	W	Th
◯	◯	◯	◯
W/C goal: W/C actual:	W/C goal: W/C actual:	W/C goal: W/C actual:	W/C goal: W/C actual:
◯	◯	◯	◯
W/C goal: W/C actual:	W/C goal: W/C actual:	W/C goal: W/C actual:	W/C goal: W/C actual:
◯	◯	◯	◯
W/C goal: W/C actual:	W/C goal: W/C actual:	W/C goal: W/C actual:	W/C goal: W/C actual:
◯	◯	◯	◯
W/C goal: W/C actual:	W/C goal: W/C actual:	W/C goal: W/C actual:	W/C goal: W/C actual:
◯	◯	◯	◯
W/C goal: W/C actual:	W/C goal: W/C actual:	W/C goal: W/C actual:	W/C goal: W/C actual:
◯	◯	◯	◯
W/C goal: W/C actual:	W/C goal: W/C actual:	W/C goal: W/C actual:	W/C goal: W/C actual:

Weekly W/C goal:

....

Daily W/C goal:

....

For the month of:

F	S	Su	To-Do Research, write, Brainstorm etc
⬭	⬭	⬭	☐ ☐ ☐
W/C goal: W/C actual:	W/C goal: W/C actual:	W/C goal: W/C actual:	
⬭	⬭	⬭	☐ ☐ ☐
W/C goal: W/C actual:	W/C goal: W/C actual:	W/C goal: W/C actual:	
⬭	⬭	⬭	☐ ☐ ☐
W/C goal: W/C actual:	W/C goal: W/C actual:	W/C goal: W/C actual:	
⬭	⬭	⬭	☐ ☐ ☐
W/C goal: W/C actual:	W/C goal: W/C actual:	W/C goal: W/C actual:	
⬭	⬭	⬭	☐ ☐ ☐
W/C goal: W/C actual:	W/C goal: W/C actual:	W/C goal: W/C actual:	
⬭	⬭	⬭	☐ ☐ ☐
W/C goal: W/C actual:	W/C goal: W/C actual:	W/C goal: W/C actual:	

Notes

Notes

Notes

Notes

Scrapbook

Scrapbook

Scrapbook

Scrapbook

Scrapbook

Thank you!

Get the worksheets in PDF so you can reprint any sheet at home.

Visit www.authorzoo.com.au/thank-you
to receive your 50% off discount code to use at
https://www.etsy.com/au/shop/AuthorZoo

Thanks again, and we wish you
good luck with your story.

Made in the USA
San Bernardino, CA
20 March 2020

66110989R10062